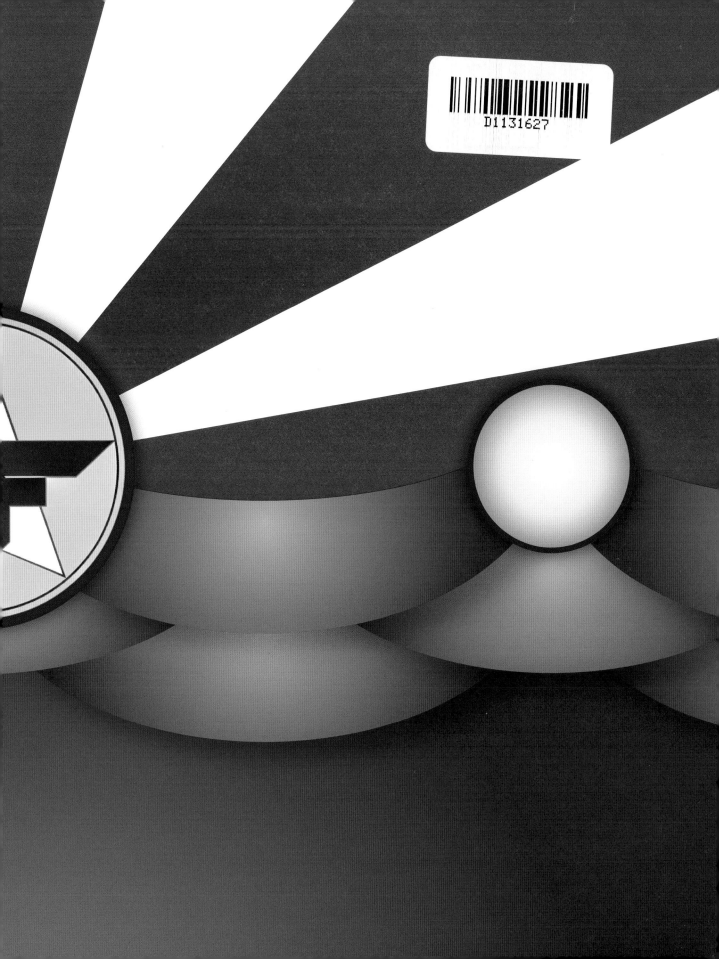

Dedicated to the stars and the stripes and the colors that bond them together

www.mascotbooks.com

Founders Force George Washington: Winged Warrior and the Delaware River

For more information, please contact:
Mascot Books
560 Herndon Parkway #120
Herndon, VA 20170
info@mascotbooks.com

Library of Congress Control Number: 2015903483

CPSIA Code: PRT0415A
ISBN-13: 978-1-63177-069-2

Printed in the United States…'Merica!

FOUNDERS FORCE

George Washington

Winged Warrior and the Delaware River

Written by
Kyle and Brandi McElhaney

Illustrated by
Michael Nozinich

GEORGE WASHINGTON WAS A TYPICAL SIX-YEAR-OLD BOY. HE HAD A SHINY, NEW HATCHET FROM HIS DAD, AND WAS TOLD TO STAY AWAY FROM THE FAMILY'S PRIZED CHERRY TREE.

WHEN GEORGE GREW UP, HE AND HIS FRIENDS WORKED IN THE CONTINENTAL CONGRESS.

They tried to help their new country grow, but kept being robbed by the villainous King, who lived far away in his big, dark castle.

GEORGE AND HIS FRIENDS DECIDED, ONCE AND FOR ALL, THEY WERE GOING TO DEFEAT THE KING. BUT FIRST, THEY NEEDED A LEADER. IT WAS TIME FOR GEORGE TO STEP UP.

THE CONGRESSIONAL MEMBERS CALLED OUT TO HIM.

"WIN FREEDOM, GEORGE!"

"WE'LL FOLLOW YOU ANYWHERE!"

"WINGED WARRIOR TO THE RESCUE!"

THE EVIL KING HEARD OF GEORGE AND HIS FRIENDS' PLANS. HE SENT SHIPS FULL OF RED-COATED SOLDIERS AND SPECIALLY-TRAINED WARRIORS TO REGAIN CONTROL OF THE COLONIES. THE KING WAS READY TO FIGHT THE AMERICAN PATRIOTS.

IT WAS THE JOB OF THE KING'S MOST CLEVER AND COLDBLOODED OFFICER, GENERAL HOWE, TO TAKE THE CITY. HIS ARMY WAS HUGE AND WAS TOO OVERPOWERING FOR WINGED WARRIOR AND HIS FRIENDS TO FIGHT. THEY HAD TO MOVE UNTIL THE TIME WAS RIGHT.

AFTER MOVING THREE TIMES TO ENSURE THE BEST FORCE POSSIBLE, WINGED WARRIOR'S FRIENDS WERE SCARED ALL WOULD BE LOST.

BUT GIVING UP WOULD ONLY MAKE THEIR FREEDOM COME MORE SLOWLY. THEY ALL TRAINED, WORKED HARD, AND FINALLY...IT WAS TIME!

WINGED WARRIOR AND HIS FRIENDS SET UP CAMP ON ONE SIDE OF THE DELAWARE RIVER, ACROSS FROM THE CRUELEST OF THE KING'S SOLDIERS. WINGED WARRIOR, SENSING THEIR NERVOUSNESS, CALLED HIS LEADERS TOGETHER. "DISCIPLINE IS THE SOUL OF AN ARMY. IT MAKES SMALL NUMBERS FORMIDABLE; PROCURES SUCCESS TO THE WEAK, AND ESTEEM TO ALL!"

All of Winged Warrior's friends were cold as they loaded up into boats to cross the river in the darkest hour of the night. Winged Warrior's giant wings spread out and glided across the river, leaving behind a trail of stars, stripes, and glory. The men were calmed by the confidence of Winged Warrior and leadership under his wings. They knew freedom was a fight away.

WINGED WARRIOR AND HIS FRIENDS ARRIVED ON THE BEACH AND STORMED THE ENEMY'S CAMP. THEY FOUGHT, THEY SHOT, THEY SWUNG, THEY CAPTURED! BEFORE THEY KNEW IT, 1,000 OF HOWE'S MOST ELITE SOLDIERS WERE IMPRISONED BY AMERICAN DETERMINATION.

As Winged Warrior's friends drifted off to peaceful sleep that night knowing they had defeated the bad guys and helped their friends and families get one step closer to freedom, Winged Warrior prayed that one day his friends and the whole country would see how strong and powerful they really are if they just keep going.

"OUR CAUSE IS NOBLE;

IT IS THE CAUSE OF MANKIND!"

About the Authors

BRANDI AND KYLE McELHANEY ARE NATIVE MISSISSIPPIANS WHO BOTH GRADUATED FROM OLE MISS. KYLE IS A CAPTAIN IN THE US ARMY AND THEY ARE BOTH INDEPENDENT DISTRIBUTORS OF HEALTH AND WELLNESS PRODUCTS. THEY HAVE TWO BOYS THAT ADORE SUPERHEROES. KYLE HAS A LOVE FOR EARLY AMERICAN HISTORY AND BRANDI HAS A PASSION FOR WHIMSY. WITH ALL THEIR POWERS COMBINED, THE *FOUNDERS FORCE* SERIES WAS CREATED. THEIR GOAL IS TO STRENGTHEN THE AMERICAN FAMILY AND CREATE A NEW GENERATION OF PATRIOTS.

About the Illustrator

Michael Nozinich is an illustrator and graphic designer living in Los Angeles, California. He is originally from Memphis, Tennessee and graduated with a Bachelor of Fine Arts from the University of Mississippi. Michael is passionate about art as well as being an avid sports fan, gamer, and all-around nerd.

Have a book idea?

Contact us at:

Mascot Books

560 Herndon Parkway

Suite 120

Herndon, VA

info@mascotbooks.com | www.mascotbooks.com